D1193045

Zippy the Squirrel

by Jeremiah Dane

Illustrated by Ira Litvin

Published 2021

ISBN: 9781513682877
ISBN (hardcover): 9781513682884
ebook ISBN: 9781513682891

Dedication

This book is dedicated to all of those who feel like they are different or feel like they don't fit in; For those that may be dissappointed with themselves for the way they are; For those that feel like they aren't enough and dream to be just like everyone else.
It's OK not to fit in. It's OK to be different. That's what makes you amazing and unique. Keep being who you are because you are enough and you are special for a reason. One day I hope you learn what that reason is, and if you look, I'm sure you'll find it.

It was bright and sunny in the forest that day,
As Zippy the Squirrel went outside to play.
He climbed on the branches and scurried through the trees
And he stopped for a minute to feel the cool breeze.

Winter was coming and he knew he would need
To gather some fruit, some nuts and some seeds
Because once the snow came, he would need food
So he could stay in his nest and have things to chew.

When he found a nut he got really excited,
He'd pick it up and run down the tree to hide it.
But one thing about Zippy is that he could never remember,
Where he had buried the nut when it came to December.

So Zippy made a visit, to the wisest he knew
To ask Hootie the Owl for an idea or two.
"Where is the last place you saw it?" asked the wise owl
But Zippy had buried so many, that it just made him scowl.

Why did he have to be this way? Zippy felt rather ashamed
Some animals thought he was silly and called him names
But some of his friends, knew his struggle was real
And brought him some nuts, seeds, and an orange peel.

But Zippy the squirrel still felt broken inside
"What is wrong with me" he often would cry.
"I just want to change so that people will like me"
So he did his best, still feeling that change was highly unlikely.

Now It was time to gather, for the forest animal meeting
And Hootie the Owl gave them all a big greeting
"There is a big concern that we need to discuss"
"And I'm afraid it's going to cause a big Fuss".

"The loggers are coming, the men with their trucks
To cut down the trees to make a few bucks
Now who's going to stop them, and where will we go?
When the trees are all gone, and we're covered in snow?"

Everyone looked at the moose and the bear,
Because Moose was so big, and bear had teeth that could scare
But Moose didn't stand a chance against the machines
And bear was going to be hibernating.

So the animals left the meeting quite concerned
About all this new information they learned.
While Hootie the Owl flew over the bend
Looking for a new home for him and his friends.

The animals were sad that they were losing their trees
And were afraid that without them they were likely to freeze.
When all of a sudden they heard Hootie's HOOT sound
Signalling the animals to gather around.

"I've found a whole forest that's full of new trees"
Said Hootie the Owl, "so we won't have to leave"
The animals rejoiced, "Who did this?" they asked,
"How could someone build a whole forest this fast?"

"It wasn't me" said the moose, "I've got these giant round feet"
"It wasn't me" said the bear, "I was fast asleep"
"I know who it was", said Hootie the Owl
"And it wasn't a deer, a rabbit or fowl"

"It was Zippy the Squirrel, who after all of this time
Was burying nuts that he never could find.
Those nuts grew into trees, and created a new forest home
Where now we can live, and call it our own."

Now when Zippy heard this, he was quite relieved
To know he wasn't as silly as the animals believed
He knew he was different, he just didn't know why
And it wasn't something he could change no matter how hard he tried.

Just like Zippy the Squirrel you are special and rare,
And you should always treat yourself with love and great care.
Accept yourself for the way that you are,
And being kind to others will help you go far.

Your friends will be there to lend you a hand,
And remember to ask for help when you can
But don't beat yourself up, if you're not like everyone else
Just love who you are, and always be yourself.

YOU ARE BEAUTIFUL AND AMAZING JUST THE WAY YOU ARE! ~ZIPPY

The End
And also the Beginning

About the author

Jeremiah Dane is a Certified Life, Relationship, and Health and Wellness Coach. As a former school teacher and lifelong learner, he is passionate about teaching and practicing the skill of positive self talk at any age.

For coaching services or to learn more, please visit:

www.thejeremiahdane.com

Made in the USA
Las Vegas, NV
14 May 2022